Guest Spot

Play-along for Flute
KIDS' MUSICALS

Wise Publications
part of The Music Sales Group
London/New York/Paris/Sydney/Copenhagen/Berlin/Madrid/Tokyo

Published by
Wise Publications
14-15 Berners Street, London W1T 3LJ, UK.

Exclusive Distributors:
Music Sales Limited
Distribution Centre, Newmarket Road, Bury St Edmunds,
Suffolk IP33 3YB, UK.
Music Sales Pty Limited
120 Rothschild Avenue, Rosebery, NSW 2018, Australia.

Order No. AM995918
ISBN 13: 978-1-84772-814-2

Arranging and engravings supplied by Camden Music.
Edited by Fiona Bolton.
Compiled by Nick Crispin.

CD recorded, mixed and mastered by Jonas Persson.
Flute played by Howard McGill.

Printed in the EU.

Flute Fingering Chart

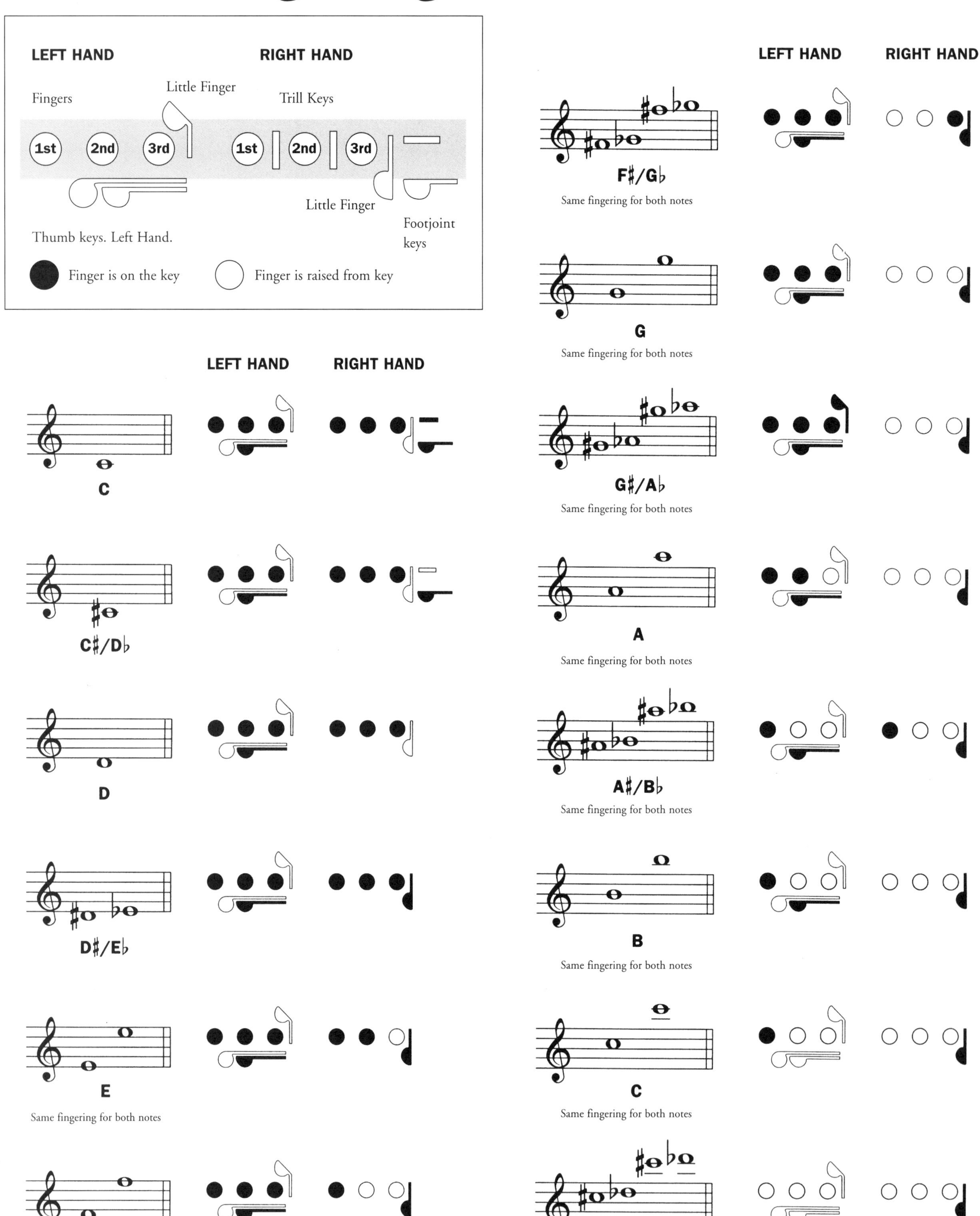

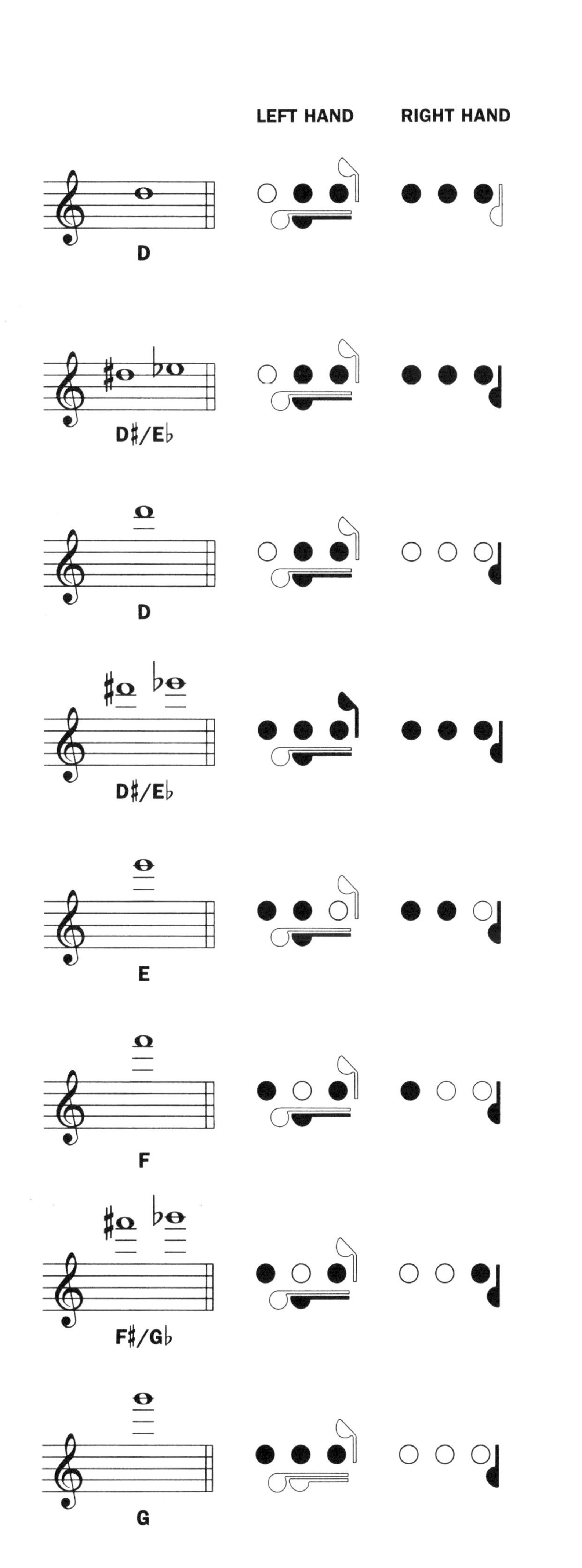
LEFT HAND
RIGHT HAND
D
D♯/E♭
D
D♯/E♭
E
F
F♯/G♭
G

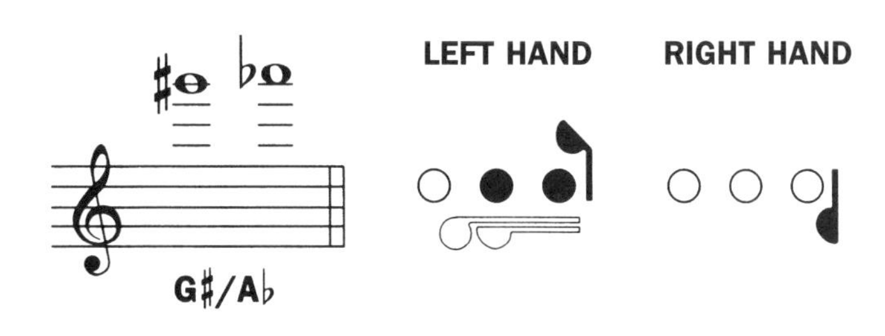
LEFT HAND
RIGHT HAND
G♯/A♭

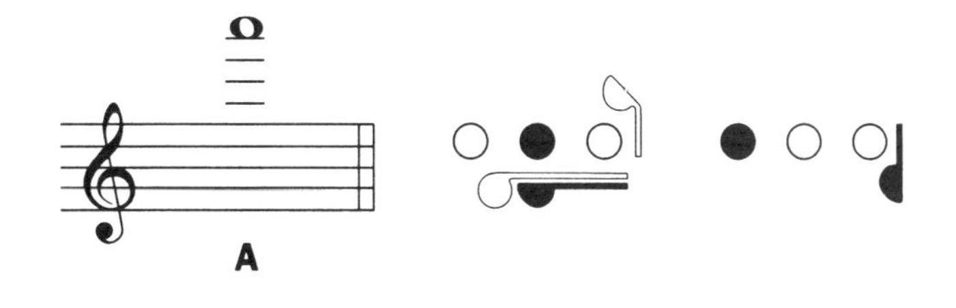
A

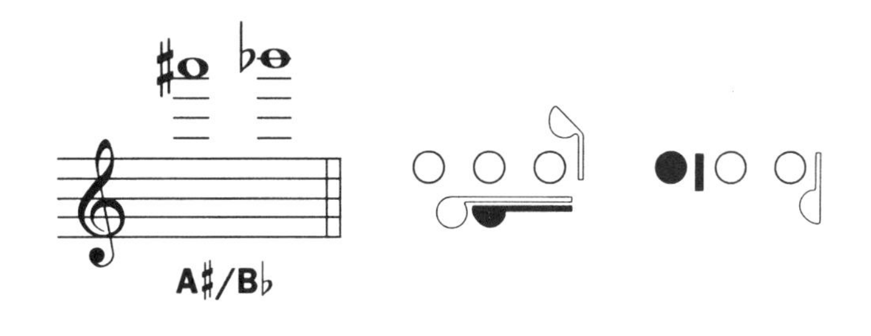
A♯/B♭

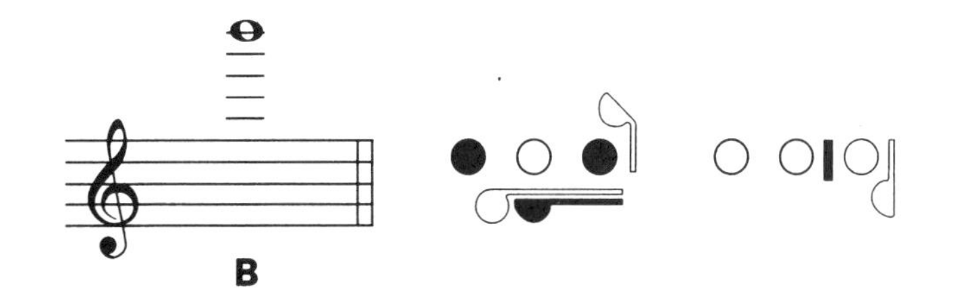
B

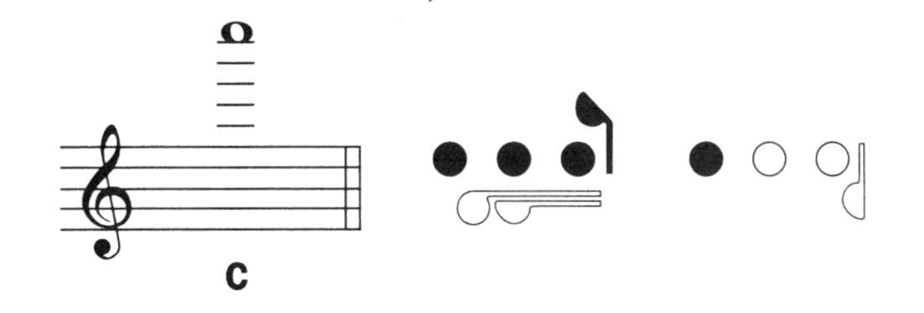
C

As Long As He Needs Me (from 'Oliver!')

Words & Music by Lionel Bart

Con moto 𝅗𝅥 = 76
31
mf
rit. poco a poco
35
molto rit.
SLOW
f
mp
Moderato ♩ = 108
40
45
50
cresc. poco a poco
p
Poco meno mosso (♩ = 100)
56
molto rit.
cresc. poco a poco
f
A tempo, più mosso ♩ = 112
60
NAT
f espressivo
Meno mosso ♩ = 104
65
MUCH
molto rit.
ff

Benjamin Calypso
(from 'Joseph And The Amazing Technicolor® Dreamcoat')

Words by Tim Rice
Music by Andrew Lloyd Webber

35
f
39
43
to Coda
47
51
55
59
D.S. al Coda
Coda
62
3
67
71
ff

Breaking Free (from 'High School Musical On Stage!')

Words & Music by Jamie Houston

31
mf
35
39
44
f
48
52

56

60
64
67
ff
71
75
f
79
83
mp dolce
molto rit.
87

Chim Chim Cher-ee (from 'Mary Poppins')

Words & Music by Richard M. Sherman & Robert B. Sherman

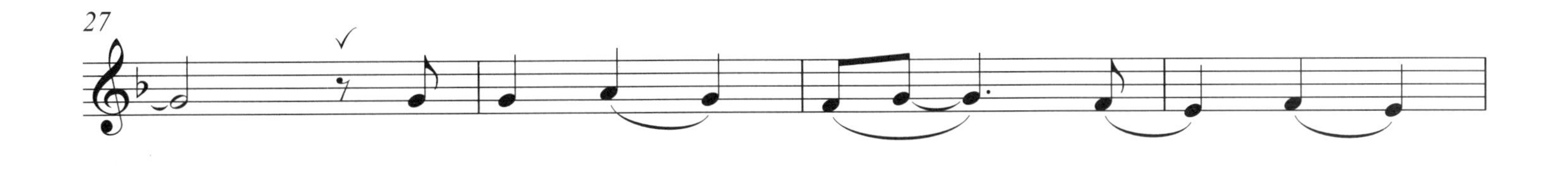

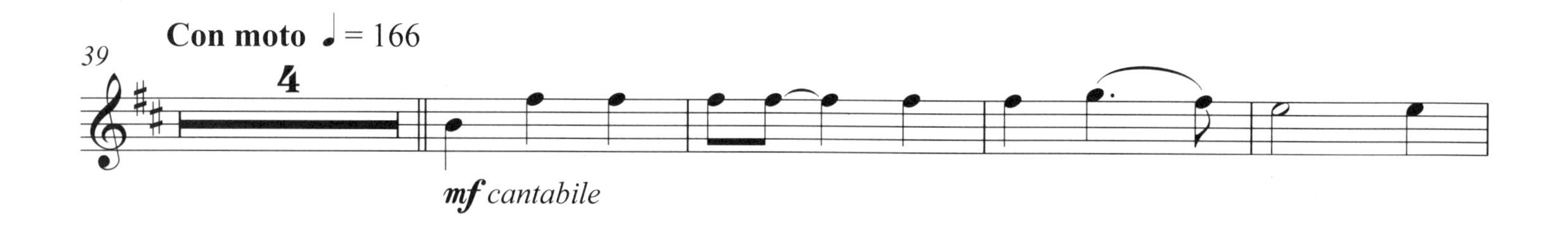
Con moto ♩ = 166
39
4
mf cantabile

47

52

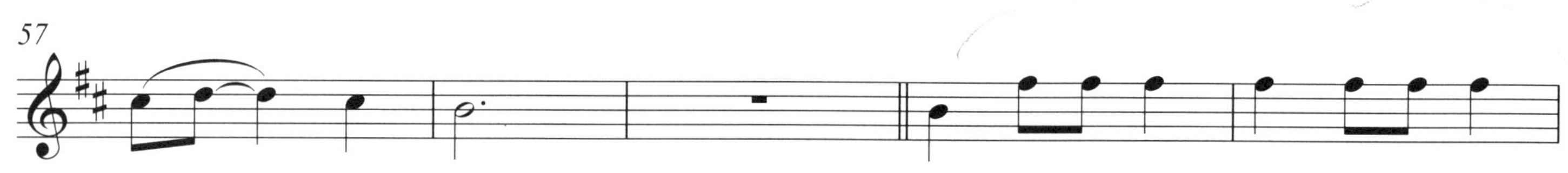
57

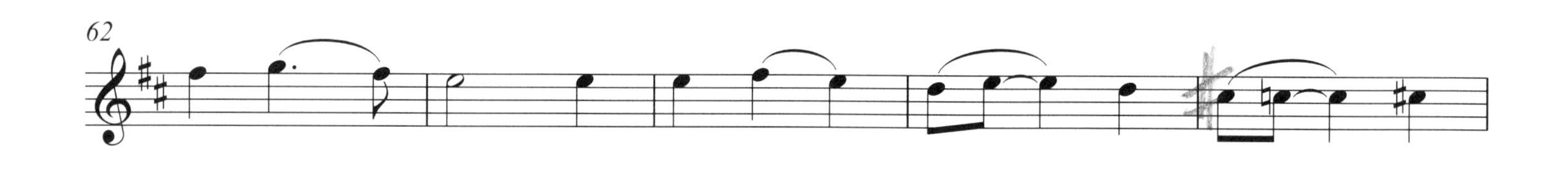
62

67

72

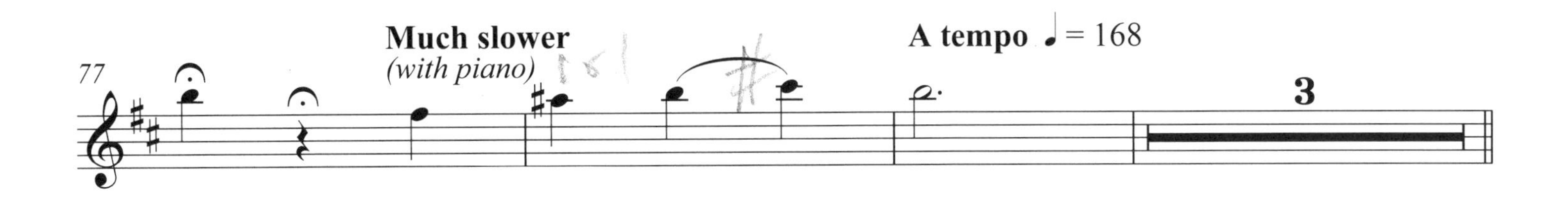
77
Much slower
(with piano)
A tempo ♩ = 168
3

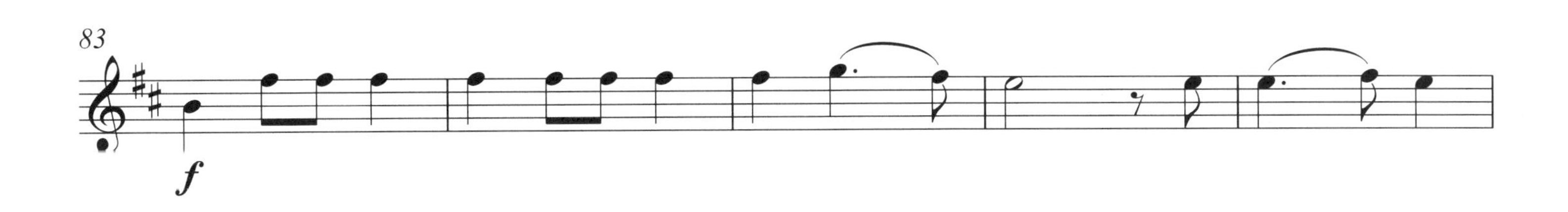
83
f

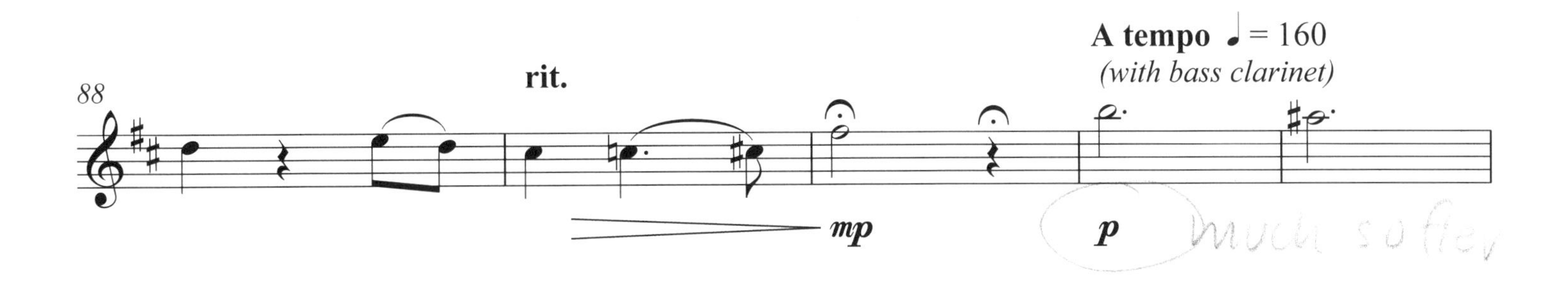
88
rit.
mp
A tempo ♩ = 160
(with bass clarinet)
p

93

98

104
rit. poco a poco
f

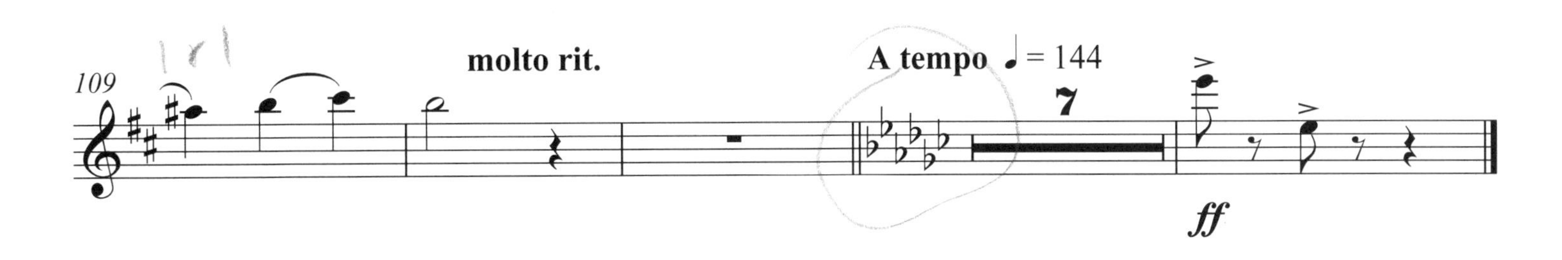
109
molto rit.
A tempo ♩ = 144
7
ff

Can You Feel The Love Tonight
(from 'The Lion King')

Words by Tim Rice
Music by Elton John

29
4
p
35
38
41
f legato
46
50
ALL
54
F
58
p
poco rit.

Electricity (from 'Billy Elliot: The Musical')

Words by Lee Hall
Music by Elton John

mf
mp
f espressivo
mf
molto rit.
Energetically ♩ = 120

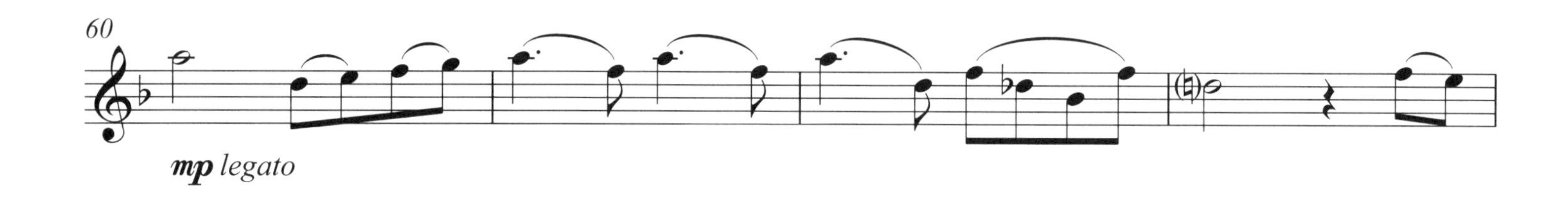
60
mp legato

64
4

72
mf

76

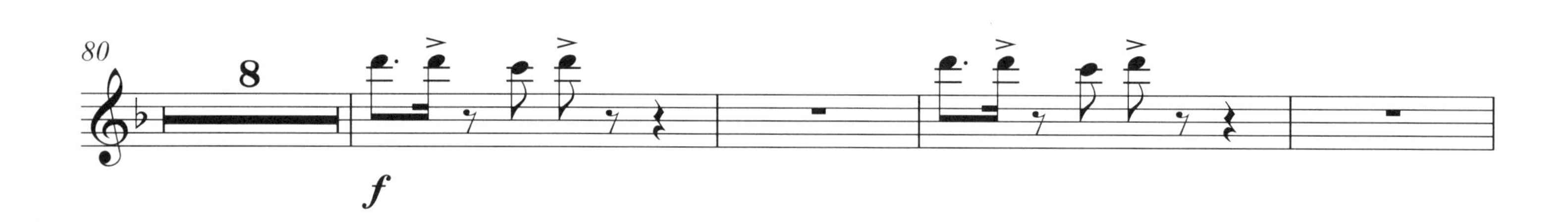
80
8
f

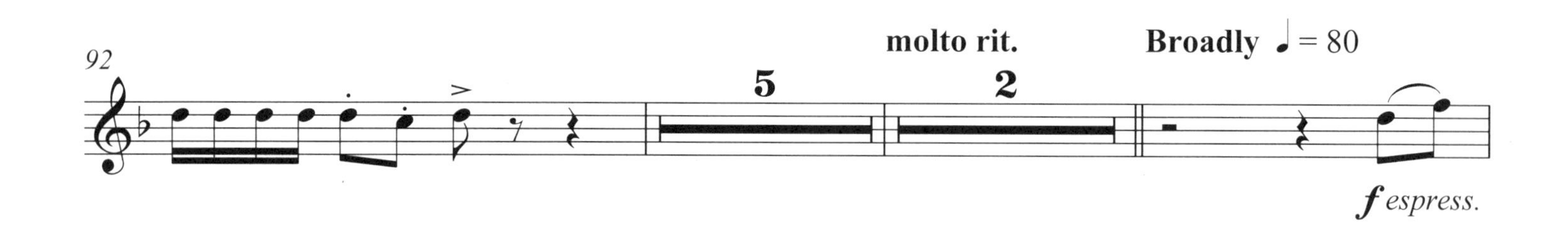
92
molto rit.
Broadly ♩ = 80
5
2
f espress.

101
3

104
107
110
3
mp
114
f espressivo
117
120
mf
123
3
f
molto rit.
a tempo
127

The Lonely Goatherd (from 'The Sound Of Music')

Words by Oscar Hammerstein II
Music by Richard Rodgers

Briskly 𝅗𝅥 = 100

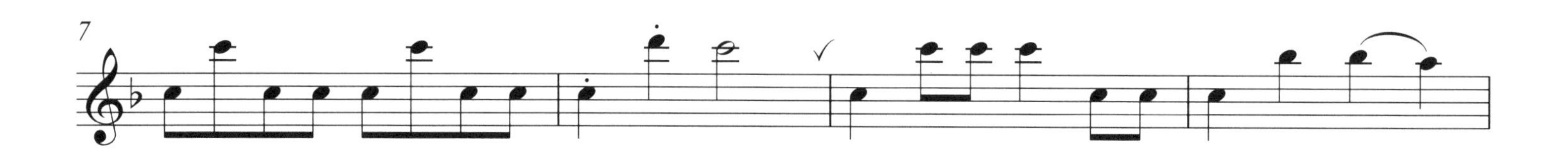

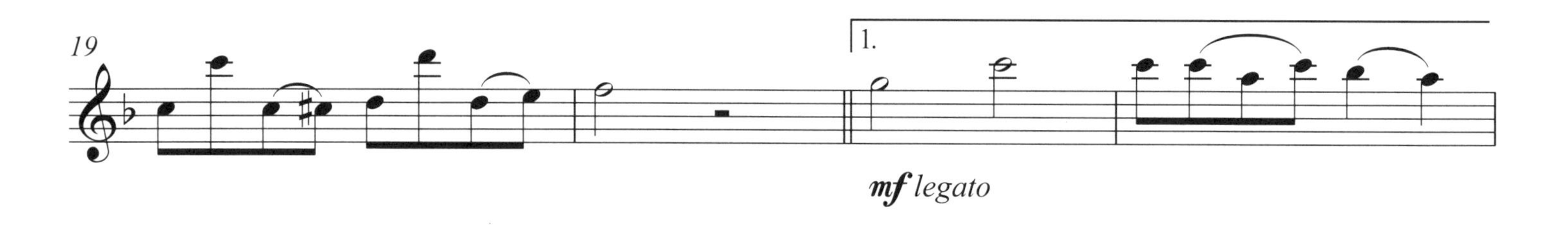

37
mf leggiero
41
45
f
49
8
61
mf
65
legato
69
73
f

So You Wanna Be A Boxer (from 'Bugsy Malone')

Words & Music by Paul Williams

26
29
32
3
38
41
44
47
50
53
3
f

Tomorrow (from 'Annie')

Words by Martin Charnin
Music by Charles Strouse

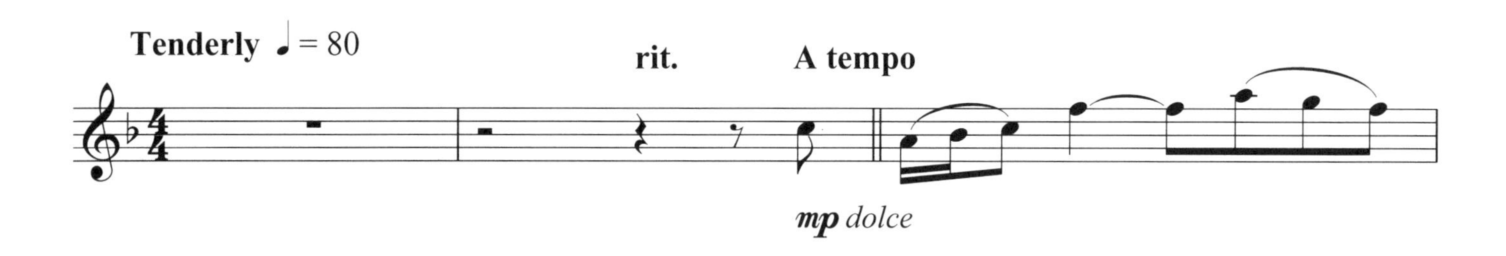

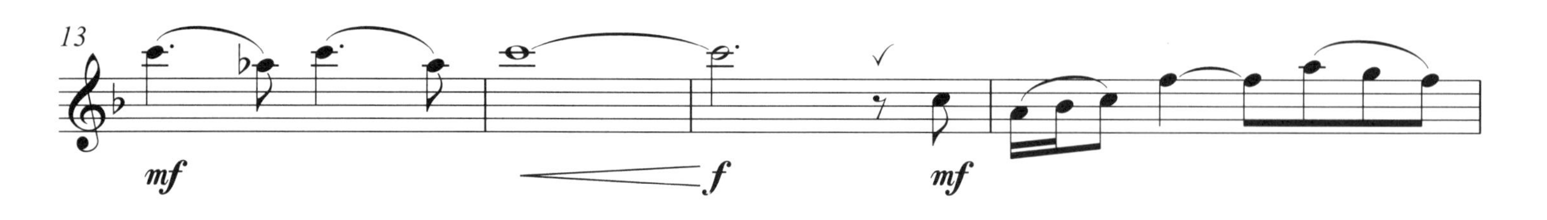

17
f

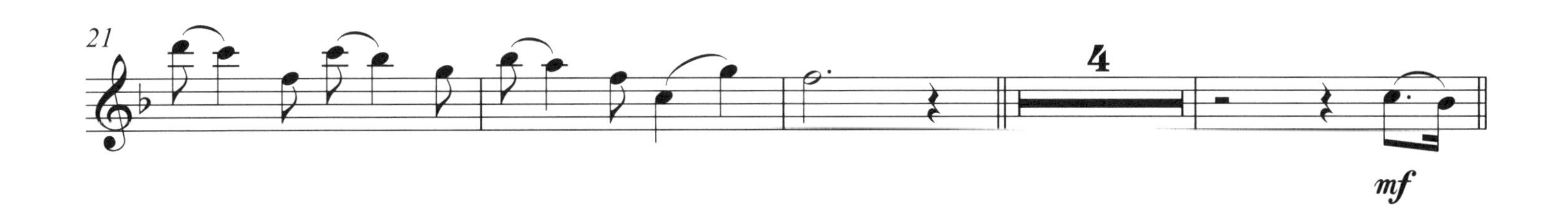
21
4
mf

29

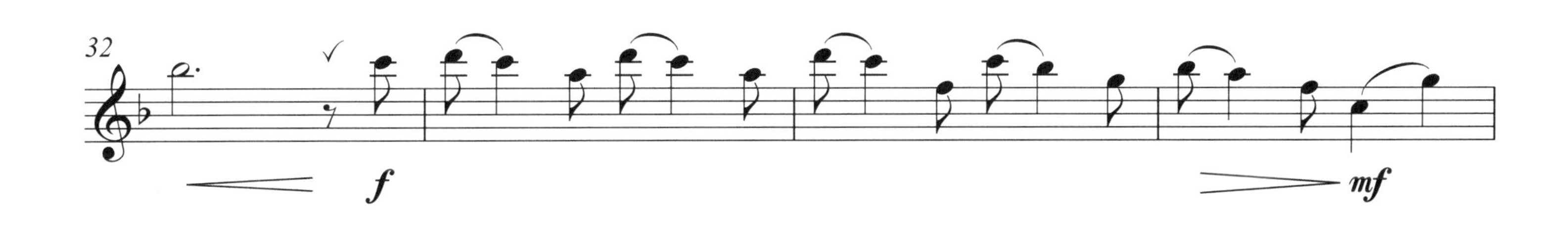
32
f
mf

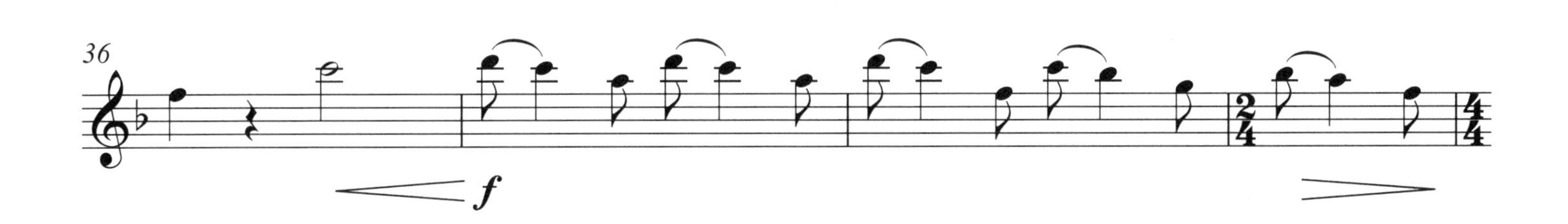
36
f

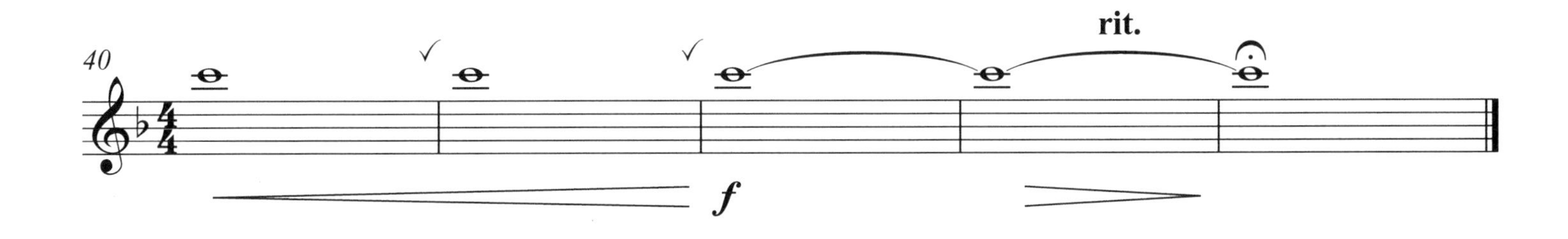
40
rit.
f

The Candy Man
(from 'Willy Wonka & The Chocolate Factory')

Words & Music by Leslie Bricusse & Anthony Newley

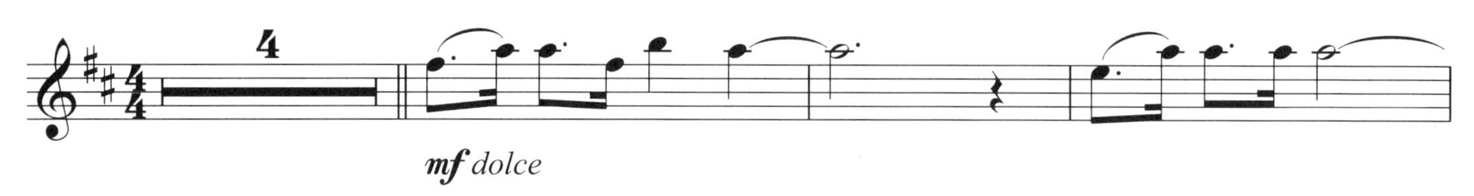

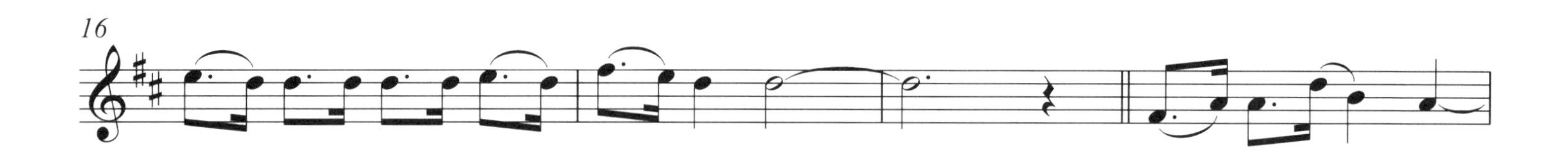

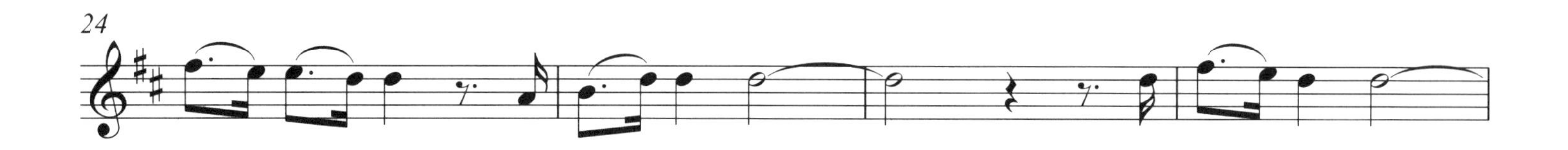

32
f
36
40
2
mf
45
49
53
57
61

65
2
f

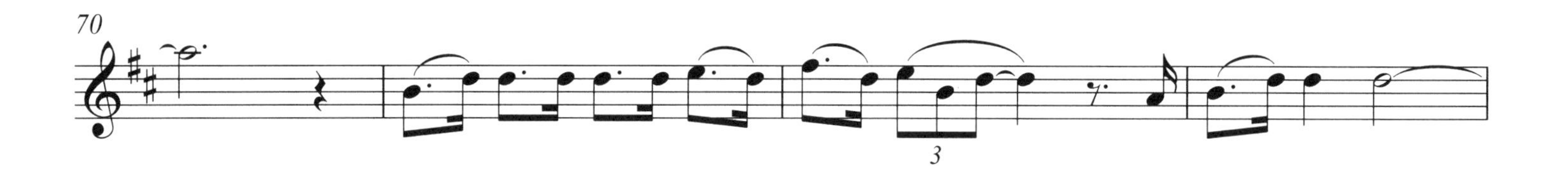
70
3

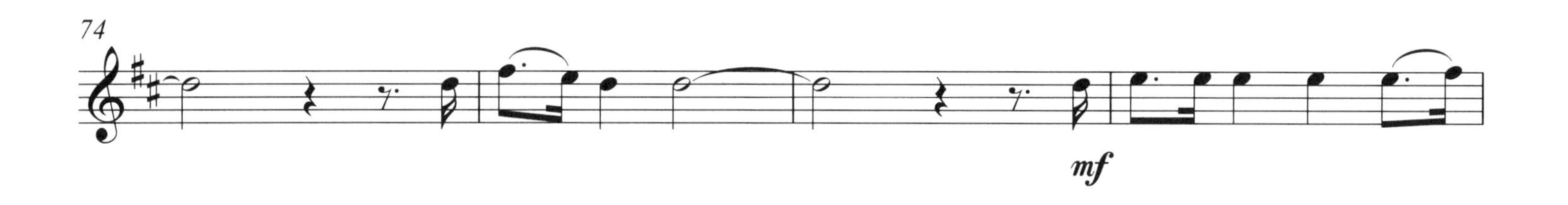
74
mf

78
molto rit.
mp dolce

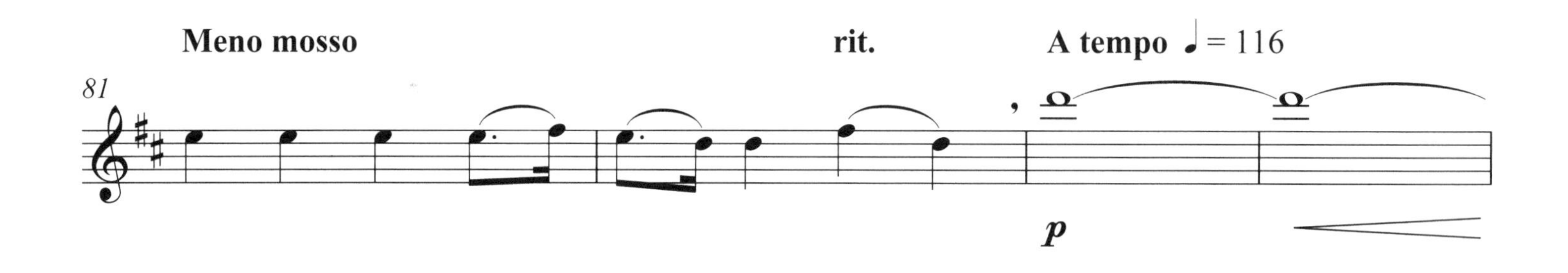
Meno mosso
rit.
A tempo ♩ = 116
81
p

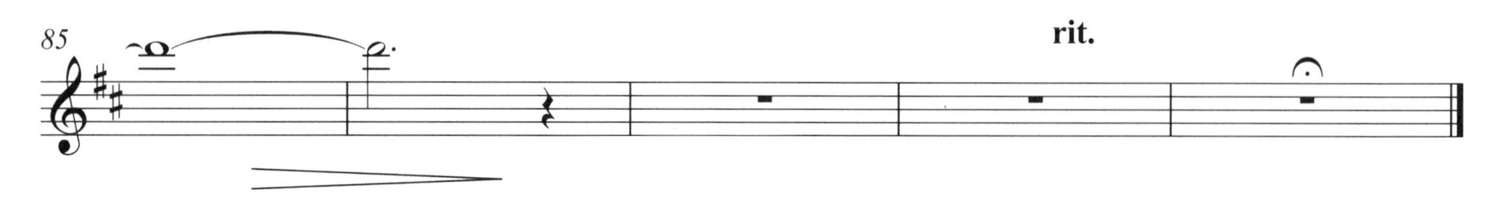
85
rit.

1 2 3 4 5 6 7 8 9

CD Track Listing

Full instrumental performances...

1. Tuning notes
2. As Long As He Needs Me
(Bart) Lakeview Music Publishing Company Limited.
3. Benjamin Calypso
(Lloyd Webber/Rice) The Really Useful Group Limited.
4. Breaking Free
(Houston) Warner/Chappell Artemis Music.
5. Chim Chim Cher-ee
(Sherman/Sherman) Warner/Chappell Artemis Music.
6. Can You Feel The Love Tonight
(Rice/John) Warner/Chappell Artemis Music.
7. Electricity
(Hall/John) Universal Music Publishing Limited.
8. The Lonely Goatherd
(Rodgers/Hammerstein II) EMI Music Publishing Limited.
9. So You Wanna Be A Boxer
(Williams) Chappell Music Limited.
10. Tomorrow
(Charnin/Strouse) Warner/Chappell Music Limited.
11. The Candy Man
(Bricusse/Newley) Universal Music Publishing Limited.

Backing tracks only...

12. As Long As He Needs Me
13. Benjamin Calypso
14. Breaking Free
15. Chim Chim Cher-ee
16. Can You Feel The Love Tonight
17. Electricity
18. The Lonely Goatherd
19. So You Wanna Be A Boxer
20. Tomorrow
21. The Candy Man